3rd Edition

FULL VOICE

WORKBOOK SERIES

INTRODUCTORY LEVEL

Researched and Developed
by Nikki Loney and Mim Adams

www.thefullvoice.com

FULL VOICE music

© COPYRIGHT 2018 FULL VOICE MUSIC
All Rights Reserved
ISBN: 978-1-897539-12-5
FVM-IL

Welcome to the 3rd Edition FULL VOICE Workbook Series

These workbooks have been researched and developed for singers working with a vocal teacher in private or classroom lessons. Every FULL VOICE lesson has fun and educational activities that encourage vocal students to sing, listen, read and write music. These workbooks complement any lesson regardless of the teaching style or repertoire preferred by student or teacher.

Introductory Level - For students ages 5-7 who are new to music lessons.

Level One - For students who have completed the Introductory Level, or the starting level for students ages 7 and up who have introductory music lesson experience (private, classroom or choral). Also suitable for older students who are new to music lessons.

Level Two - For students who have completed Level One, or students who are confident counting eighth notes and sight singing in C Major.

Level Three - For students who have completed Level Two, or students who are confident counting dotted quarter notes, singing and identifying intervals and sight singing in C, F, and G Major.

The FULL VOICE Teacher Guide

A soft cover book with 102 pages of teaching inspiration and strategies for the private voice teacher. It includes:

- simple and effective teaching strategies that you can use immediately.
- helpful strategies for getting started with new students and first lessons.
- multi-sensory warm-up activities for singers of all abilities.
- MORE singing games for beginner singers to help develop independent singing skills from the very first lesson.
- NEW! FULL VOICE Small group lesson curriculum and planning.
- NEW! Age appropriate repertoire recommendations for young singers.

Acknowledgements

Thank you to all the students, teachers, and parents who have participated in the FULL VOICE test groups over the past ten years. We are truly grateful to all the print music specialists and music retailers that have supported the FULL VOICE Workbook Series since the first edition printing in 2004.

Respect copyright

FVM-IL	ISBN	978-1-897539-12-5	FULL VOICE Workbook - Introductory Level
FVM-L1	ISBN	978-1-897539-13-2	FULL VOICE Workbook - Level One
FVM-L2	ISBN	978-1-897539-14-9	FULL VOICE Workbook - Level Two
FVM-L3	ISBN	978-1-897539-15-6	FULL VOICE Workbook - Level Three

TABLE OF CONTENTS

TONIC SOL-FA: DO TO MI

Date: _____

Tonic sol-fa is a singing method that uses words and hand signs for every note in a scale. Tonic sol-fa is very easy to learn and helps singers to sing out confidently. Tonic sol-fa is also a fun activity. Your **FULL VOICE** workbook has lots of tonic sol-fa games and activities for you to try with your teacher, classmates and parents.

Here are the first three hand signs of the **tonic sol-fa** scale.

Your teacher will show you how to sing and sign them.

1. Sing and sign the first three notes of the scale with your teacher slowly.

   a) Sing and sign **repeating** notes.

Repeating notes stay at the same pitch.

   b) Sing and sign **ascending** notes.

Ascending means that the pitch moves **higher**.

   c) Sing and sign **descending** notes.

Descending means that the pitch moves **lower**.

2. Write the name of the hand sign then sing the following melodies.

a)

_____ _____ _____ _____ _____

b)

_____ _____ _____ _____ _____

3. Fill in the missing tonic sol-fa syllable.

a)
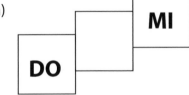

b)
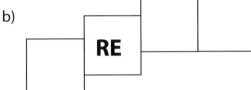

c)
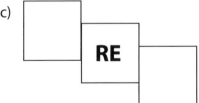

d)
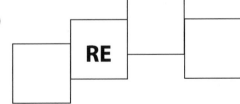

LESSON REVIEW: TONIC SOL-FA DO TO MI

1. Sing and sign **DO** to **MI** ascending from memory. *(1 mark)*

2. Sing and sign **DO** to **MI** descending from memory. *(1 mark)*

3. Sing and sign **DO** to **MI** ascending and descending from memory. *(2 marks)*

4. Listen to your teacher play a different starting note on the piano.

   Can you sing **DO** to **MI** after hearing the new starting note? *(1 mark)*

_____
5

Lesson Two

1. Sing and sign the first five hand signs for your teacher.

a) Sing and sign **ascending** notes.

b) Sing and sign **descending** notes.

c) Sing and sign **repeating** notes.

2. Write the names of the hand signs.

a)

_____   _____   _____   _____   _____

b)

_____   _____   _____   _____   _____

3. Fill in the missing tonic sol-fa syllables in the boxes.

a)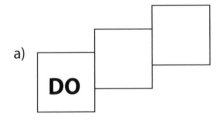
DO

b)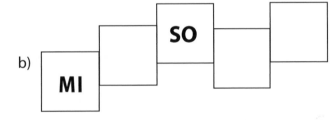
SO
MI

c)
RE

d)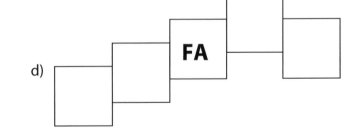
FA

LESSON REVIEW: TONIC SOL-FA DO TO SO

1. Sing and sign **DO** to **SO** ascending, from memory. *(1 mark)*

2. Sing and sign **DO** to **SO** descending, from memory. *(1 mark)*

3. Sing and sign **DO** to **SO** ascending and descending. *(2 marks)*

4. Listen to your teacher play a different starting note on the piano.

   Can you sing **DO** to **SO** after hearing the new starting note? *(1 mark)*

5

Lesson Three

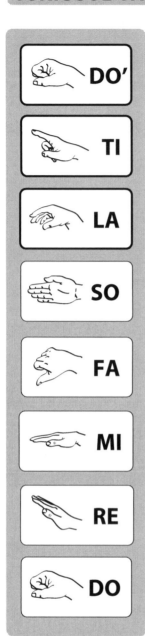

DO'

TI

LA

SO

FA

MI

RE

DO

1. 🎤 Sing and sign the entire scale **ascending** and **descending**.

2. 🎤 Sing the scale **descending** only.

3. 🎤 Sing the following patterns.

   a) Sing from **DO** to **SO**.

   b) Sing from **DO** to **FA**.

   c) Sing from **DO** to **MI**.

4. 🎤 Sing the following melodies without using hand signs.

   a) **DO**   **DO**   **DO**   **RE**   **MI**

   b) **DO**   **RE**   **MI**   **FA**   **SO**

5. ✏️ Write your own tonic sol-fa melody.

6. 🎤 Sing your melody. (Or make your teacher sing it!)

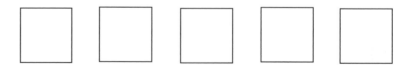

7. 🎤 Have some fun with your teacher playing the following tonic sol-fa game.

FOLLOW THE LEADER

a) Have your teacher lead you by pointing to the tonic sol-fa hand sign cards on the wall or by signing the sol-fa hand signs. Watch carefully. They can use melodies that include ascending, descending and repeating patterns. Can you follow where they go and sing the notes correctly?

b) Now you point to the tonic sol-fa hand sign cards and have your teacher sing the notes back to you. Did they sing the correct notes?

8. Write the name of the hand sign below each picture, then sing the following melodies.

a)

_____   _____   _____   _____   _____

b)

_____   _____   _____   _____   _____

9. Fill in the missing tonic sol-fa syllables in the boxes.

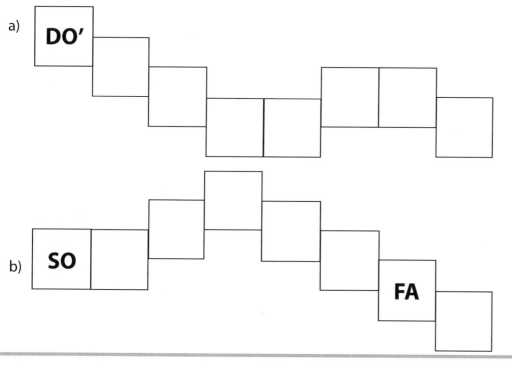

a) **DO'**

b) **SO**   **FA**

LESSON REVIEW: TONIC SOL-FA DO TO DO'

1. Sing and sign the **ascending** tonic sol-fa scale for your teacher, without looking at your book. _(5 marks)_

2. Sing and sign the **descending** tonic sol-fa scale for your teacher, without looking at your book. _(5 marks)_

$\overline{10}$

Lesson Four

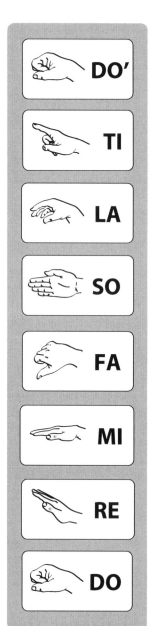

DO'

TI

LA

SO

FA

MI

RE

DO

1. Sing and sign the entire scale **ascending** and **descending**.

2. Sing the scale **descending** only.

3. Sing the following patterns.

   a) Sing from **DO** to **SO**.

   b) Sing from **SO** to **DO**.

   c) Sing from **DO** to **LA**.

4. Sing the following.

   a) **DO** **RE** **DO** **DO** **RE**

   b) **DO** **RE** **MI** **FA** **MI**

5. Write your own tonic sol-fa melody.

6. Sing your melody.

7. Have some fun with your teacher playing the following tonic sol-fa game.

COPY CAT

a) Listen to your teacher sing a 3-note tonic sol-fa melody.
   Can you sing the melody back to them correctly?

b) Sing a 3-note tonic sol-fa melody to your teacher.
   Can your teacher sing the same melody back to you?

c) Now make it more challenging by singing more notes each time.
   How many notes can you copy before you make a mistake?

Music is written using symbols called **notes**. Each note is played or sung using **"counts"** or **"beats"**. Like the ticking of a clock, the beats or counting of music is always **steady**.

quarter note

1

A quarter note is held for **one beat** or count.

1. Clap and count **quarter notes**.
2. Sing **quarter notes** using **DO**, **RE** or **MI**.
3. Practice drawing **quarter notes**.

half note

1   2

A half note is held for **two beats** or counts.

4. Clap and count **half notes**.
5. Sing **half notes**, using **DO**, **RE** or **MI**.
6. Practice drawing **half notes.**

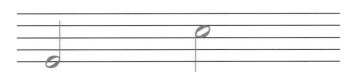

LESSON REVIEW: QUARTER NOTES AND HALF NOTES

1. Write the counts below each note. *(2 marks)*

2. Clap and count the rhythm slowly. *(3 marks)*

a)

1

5

Lesson Five

BREATHING

Date: _____

| breathing | In order to sing properly, you need to learn to breathe correctly. Singers must take deep and relaxed breaths. |

1. 💬 Have your teacher discuss and demonstrate a simple breathing exercise.

2. 🗣 Sing the tonic sol-fa scale **ascending** and **descending** using **one breath**.

Breathing Challenge

3. 👂 Listen to your teachers play the following notes on the piano.

4. 🗣 Sing the note using "loo" and hold the note for as long as you can while your teacher records the time.

5. ✏️ Write how many seconds you were able to hold each note.

a) _____ seconds   b) _____ seconds   c) _____ seconds

6. 💬 Was it easier to hold the lower note or the higher note?

7. 🗣 Have your teacher sing one of the notes above. How long can they hold it for?

CLAPPING AND COUNTING

1. ✏️ Write the counts under each note.

2. 👂 Listen to your teacher clap and count these notes aloud.

3. ✋ Clap and count the notes slowly.

a)

1   2

whole note

𝅝

1 2 3 4

A whole note is held for **4 beats** or counts.

1. Clap and count **whole notes**.

2. Sing **whole notes** using **DO**, **RE** or **MI**.

3. Practice drawing **whole notes** on the staff.

4. Write the counts under each note.

5. Clap and count the notes slowly.

1 2 3 4

LESSON REVIEW: WRITING NOTES ON THE STAFF

1. Practice writing **quarter**, **half** and **whole notes** on the staff below.

2. Write the counts below each note.

a)

b)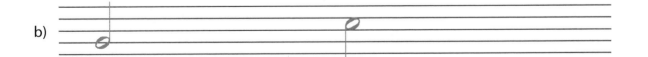

c)

Review One

TONIC SOL- FA SCALE

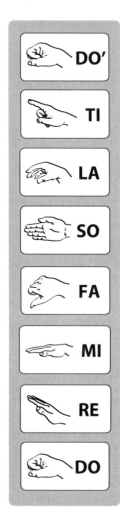

DO'	
TI	
LA	
SO	
FA	
MI	
RE	
DO	

1. Sing and sign the scale **ascending** and **descending**. *(1 mark)*

2. Sing and sign the scale **descending** and **ascending**. *(1 mark)*

3. Sing and sign the entire scale **in one breath**. *(1 mark)*

4. Sing and sign the following. *(1 mark)*

a)

5. Sing the following. *(1 mark each)*

a) **DO** **RE** **RE** **MI** **MI**

b) **DO** **RE** **MI** **FA** **SO**

6. Fill in the missing tonic sol-fa syllables in the boxes. *(4 marks)*

a)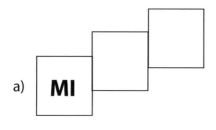
MI

b)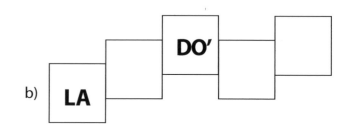
LA **DO'**

c)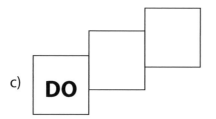
DO

d)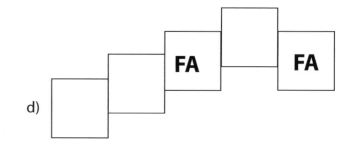
FA **FA**

1. ✏️ Draw a line to the correct note. *(1 mark each)*

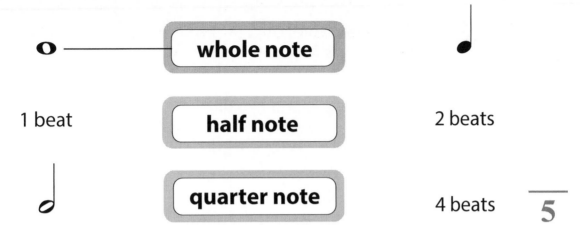

𝗈 ———	**whole note**	
1 beat	**half note**	2 beats
♩	**quarter note**	4 beats $\overline{5}$

1. ✏️ Write the counts under each note. *(1 mark each)*

2. ✋ Clap and count the notes slowly. *(2 marks each)*

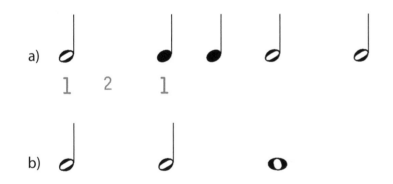

a) ♩ ♩ ♩ ♩ ♩

    1   2   1

b) ♩   ♩   𝗈

3. ✏️ Add the value of the notes. *(1 mark each)*

a) ♩ + ♩ + ♩ = _____

b) ♩ + ♩ = _____

c) ♩ + ♩ + ♩ = _____

d) ♩ + ♩ = _____ $\overline{10}$

$\overline{25}$

Lesson Six

| tempo | Tempo refers to the speed at which you are singing. Singing using different tempos can be challenging. |

DO'
TI
LA
SO
FA
MI
RE
DO

1. Review the **tonic sol-fa scale** with your teacher.

2. Sing the scale ascending and descending using different speeds

3. ✓ I can sing:

☐ the entire scale **ascending and descending**.

☐ the entire scale **ascending and descending in one breath**.

☐ the entire scale **ascending and descending using a slow tempo**.

☐ the entire scale **ascending and descending using a fast tempo**.

COUNTING AND SINGING

1. Clap and count the notes *slowly*.

2. Sing the tonic sol-fa syllable with the correct rhythm.

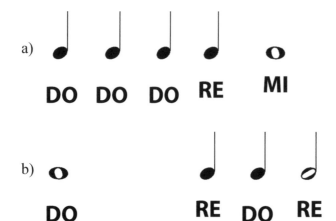

a) DO DO DO RE MI

b) DO RE DO RE

---

dotted half note

1 **2** **3**

A dotted half note is held for **three beats** or counts.

1. Clap and count **dotted half notes**.
2. Practice drawing **dotted half notes**.

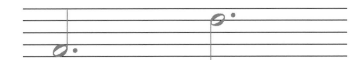

3. Write the counts under each note.
4. Clap and count the rhythms slowly.

a)

b)

LESSON REVIEW: RHYTHMS AND TONIC SOL-FA

1. Write a tonic sol-fa syllable on each line below the staff.

2. Write **quarter**, **half**, **whole** or **dotted half notes** on the staff above the sol-fa.

3. Have your teacher sing your melody. *(Give your teacher a mark out of 5!)*

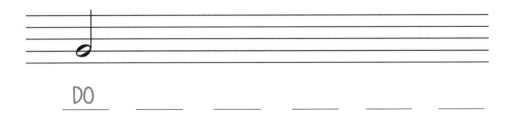

DO

5

Lesson Seven

TONIC SOL-FA

DO'
TI
LA
SO
FA
MI
RE
DO

1. Sing the tonic sol-fa scale **ascending** and **descending**.

2. Sing the tonic sol-fa scale **descending** and **ascending**.

3. Sing the following patterns.

a) **DO** **RE** **MI** **RE** **DO**

b) **DO** **RE** **MI** **FA** **SO**

c) **DO** **RE** **DO** **RE** **MI**

LISTENING ACTIVITY

1. Listen to your teacher sing one of the three note melodies below using "loo", instead of using tonic sol-fa syllables.

2. Can you identify the pattern that they sang?

a) **DO RE MI**   b) **DO DO MI**   c) **DO DO DO**

COUNTING AND SINGING

1. Sing the following notes with the correct rhythms. Keep a very slow tempo.

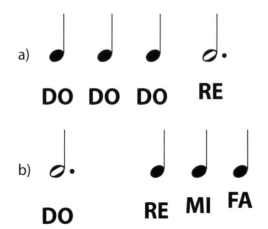

a) **DO** **DO** **DO** **RE**

b) **DO** **RE** **MI** **FA**

FULL VOICE WORKBOOK - INTRODUCTORY LEVEL

Music is written on a **staff**. This staff has five **lines** and four **spaces**.

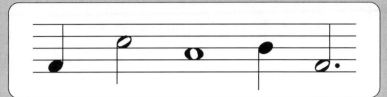

The **lines** and the **spaces** are numbered starting from the bottom and counting up.

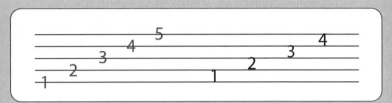

1. Circle all the notes that are written on **lines**.

2. Identify each note as a **line note** (L) or a **space note** (S).

L   ___   ___   ___   ___   ___

LESSON REVIEW: NOTES ON LINES AND SPACES

1. Draw **whole notes** on the **lines** or **spaces** indicated. *(1 mark each)*

Line 2   Space 1   Space 4   Line 3   Line 5

5

Lesson Eight

TONIC SOL- FA   Date: _____

DO'
TI
LA
SO
FA
MI
RE
DO

1. 🗣 Sing the tonic sol-fa scale **ascending** and **descending**.

2. 🗣 Sing the following patterns.

a) **DO   RE   MI   RE   MI**

b) **DO   RE   MI   FA   FA**

3. ✏ Write your own tonic sol-fa melody.
4. 🗣 Sing your melody.

☐   ☐   ☐   ☐   ☐

MUSIC NOTES REVIEW

1. ✏ Fill in the blanks.

a) ♩ This is a _____ note. It is held for _____ beat or count.

b) 𝅝 This is a _____ note. It is held for _____ beats or counts.

c) 𝅗𝅥 This is a _____ note. It is held for _____ beats or counts.

d) 𝅗𝅥• This is a _____ note. It is held for _____ beats or counts.

stems going up

If the note head is **below** the **third** line the stem goes **UP**.

1.  Draw stems going **up**.

Notes with stems going **up** look like the letter "**d**". Remember "d" for dog.

stems going down

If the note head is **above** the **third** line the stem goes **DOWN**.

2. Draw stems going **down**.

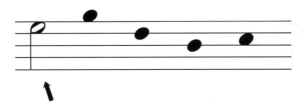

Notes with stems going **down** look like the letter "**p**". Remember "p" for puppy.

3. Add a stem to each note below.

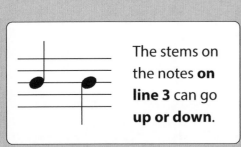
The stems on the notes **on line 3** can go **up or down**.

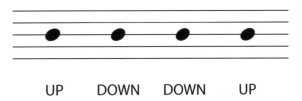

UP   DOWN   DOWN   UP

LESSON REVIEW: WRITING NOTES WITH STEMS

1. Draw **stems** on the notes below. *(1 mark each)*

5

Lesson Nine

DO'
TI
LA
SO
FA
MI
RE
DO

1. Sing the tonic sol-fa scale **ascending** and **descending**.
2. Sing the following patterns.

a) **DO** **RE** **DO** **RE** **MI**

b) **RE** **RE** **MI** **MI** **DO**

3. Write your own tonic sol-fa pattern.
4. Sing your pattern.

[ ] [ ] [ ] [ ] [ ]

COUNTING AND SINGING

1. Write your own tonic sol-fa syllables under each note.
2. Sing your melody with the correct rhythm.

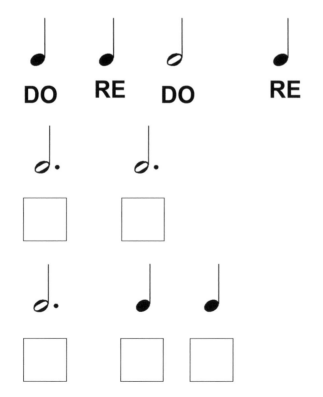

treble clef

There is a symbol that is found at the beginning of the staff. This is called a **clef**. Music for *most* singers is written using the **treble clef**.

This clef is also called the **G clef**. It is a fancy capital "**G**". When drawn onto the staff, it curls around the second line.

1. Trace the steps below to learn to draw the **treble clef**.

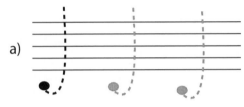

a) Start at the bottom, below the staff and draw a dot and a letter "**J**" up through and above line 5.

b) Draw a curved line, making the letter "**D**" touching line 4.

c) Cross through the letter "**J**" and draw a curved "**C**" line that touches line 1.

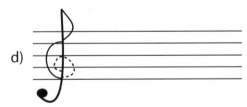

d) Cross through the letter "**J**" again and curl up and around the line 2.

LESSON REVIEW: TREBLE CLEF

1. Draw three **treble clefs** at the beginning of the staff. *(1 mark each)*

2. Draw **stems** on the note heads below. *(1 mark each)*

3. Clap and count notes aloud. *(4 marks)*

10

MUSICAL ALPHABET

Date: _____

In music, we use only the first seven letters of the alphabet. These letters repeat over and over.

A B C D E F G

1. Fill in the missing letters. Remember that they repeat over and over.

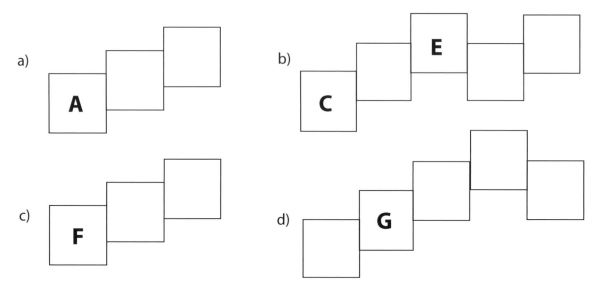

a) **A**

b) **C** **E**

c) **F**

d) **G**

NOTE NAMES ON THE MUSIC STAFF

The note names on the **music staff** move up the staff in steps. Notice how they move from **line to space to line**. These seven letters repeat over and over.

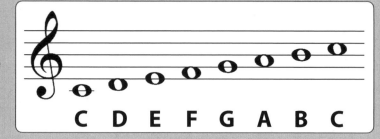

C D E F G A B C

1. Fill in the missing notes or note names in the boxes below.

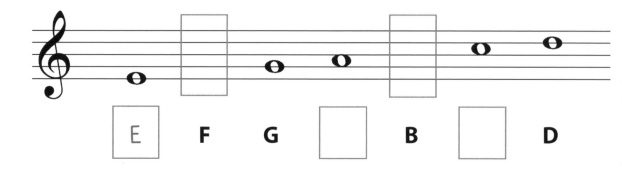

E   **F**   **G**   ☐   **B**   ☐   **D**

middle C

It sits **below** the staff and has its own line.

1. Practice drawing **middle C** on the staff.

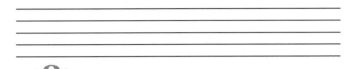

D

It sits below the staff, but is attached to it.

2. Practice drawing **D** on the staff.

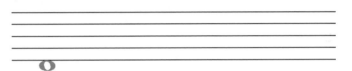

LESSON REVIEW: WRITING MUSIC ON THE STAFF

1. Draw a **treble clef** at the beginning of each staff. *(1 mark each)*

2. Draw **stems** on the note heads below. *(1 mark each)*

a)
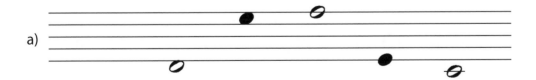

b)

12

TONIC SOL-FA

Date: _____

1. ✓ Check when completed. *(1 mark each)*

☐ I can sing the tonic sol-fa scale **ascending** and **descending**.

☐ I can sing the tonic sol-fa scale **descending** and **ascending**.

☐ I can sing the tonic sol-fa scale **ascending and descending in one breath**.

2. 🗣 Sing the following patterns. *(1 mark each)*

a) **DO RE MI RE DO**

b) **RE RE MI MI DO**

c) **RE RE RE MI DO**

3. ✏ Fill in the missing letters of the musical alphabet. *(4 marks)*

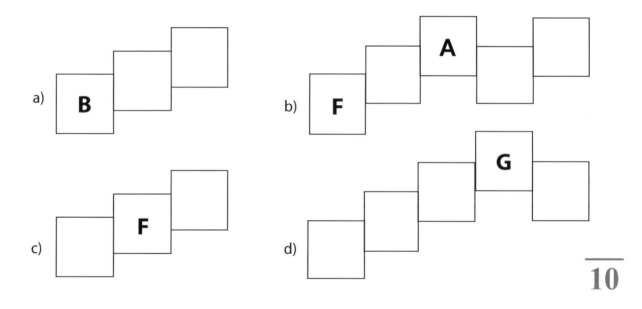

a) **B**

b) **F** **A**

c) **F**

d) **G**

$\overline{10}$

COUNTING AND SINGING

1. 🗣 Sing the following notes with the correct rhythms. Keep a very slow tempo.

a) DO RE MI FA SO

$\overline{5}$

FULL VOICE WORKBOOK - INTRODUCTORY LEVEL

1. 🖉 Draw a **treble clef**. *(1 mark)*

2. 🖉 Add stems to each note. *(3 marks)*

3. 🖉 Draw a **middle C** using a **whole note**. *(1 mark)*

4. 🖉 Draw a **D** using a **half note**. *(1 mark)*

5. 🖉 On the staff below, draw the following: *(1 mark each)*

   a) A **whole note** on **line 5**.
   b) A **quarter note** on **middle C**.
   c) A **half note** on **line 1**.
   d) A **dotted half note** on **space 4**.

   a)   b)   c)   d)

   $$\overline{10}$$

1. 🕪 Listen to your teacher clap, play or sing a short rhythmic pattern that includes **quarter, half, whole** and **dotted half notes**. *(5 marks)*

   ☐ I can clap the same rhythm back to them.

   $$\overline{5} \quad \overline{30}$$

Lesson Eleven

TECHNICAL EXERCISES

Date: _____

technical exercises

Technical exercises are short melodies that a vocalist sings repeatedly at higher and lower pitches to warm up and strengthen the voice. Exercises are an important part of your lesson.

EE AH OH OO

When singing exercises, singers use **vowel sounds**. Pay close attention to the shape of your mouth and the sound of your vowels.

1. Sing this exercise using relaxed, open vowel sounds.

a) **EE** as in **me**.   b) **AH** as in **awesome**.   c) **OH** as in **note**.   d) **OO** as in **boot**.

LEARNING LINE NOTES

The letter names of the notes on the music staff **lines** make a sentence that is easy to remember.

Every **G**ood **B**oy **D**eserves **F**un

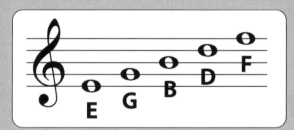

1. Draw a **treble clef** at the beginning of the staff.

2. Name the **line** notes.

____ ____ ____ ____ ____

FULL VOICE WORKBOOK - INTRODUCTORY LEVEL

3. Draw a **treble clef** at the beginning of the staff.

4. Write the following **line** notes. Use **whole notes**.

Remember that middle C is a line note too.

E   C   G   F   B   D

5. Draw a **treble clef** at the beginning of the staff.

6. Write the following **line** notes. Use **quarter notes**.

D   C   F   G   E   D

LESSON REVIEW: WRITING LINE NOTES ON THE STAFF

1. Write the sentence that you use to name the notes on the lines. *(5 marks)*

_____

2. Draw **stems** on the note heads below. *(1 mark each)*

3. Name the notes. *(1 mark each)*

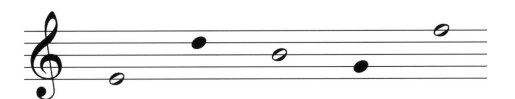

15

SINGING LEGATO

Date: _____

| legato | **Legato** means to sing **smoothly and connected.** Singers need to breathe deeply to sing legato. Your teacher will demonstrate. |

1. Sing the following exercises. Use relaxed, open vowel sounds.

a)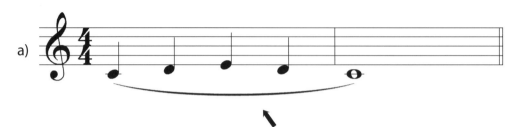

The curved line connecting the notes is called a **slur**. It tells us to sing **legato** - smooth and connected.

b)

LISTENING ACTIVITY

1. Listen carefully as your teacher plays or sings the following rhythm examples **at random.**

2. Can you identify the correct rhythm below?

a)

b)

c)

d)

FULL VOICE WORKBOOK - INTRODUCTORY LEVEL

The letter names of the notes in the **spaces** spell a word that is easy to remember:

F A C E

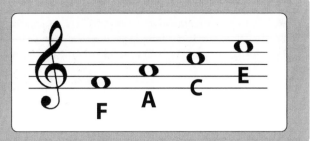

1. ✎ Draw a **treble clef** at the beginning of the staff.

2. ✎ Name the space notes.

3. ✎ Write the following notes in the **spaces**.

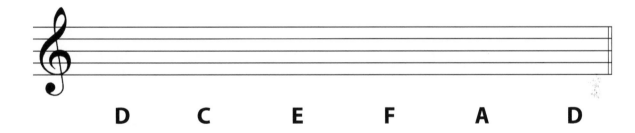

D   C   E   F   A   D

LESSON REVIEW: LEARNING SPACE NOTES

1. ✎ Draw a **treble clef** at the beginning of the staff. *(1 mark)*

2. ✎ Draw **stems** on the note heads below. *(1 mark each)*

3. ✎ Name the notes. *(1 mark each)*

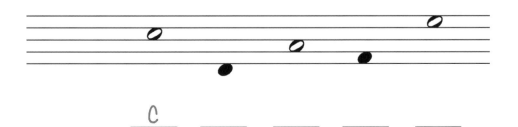

C

10

SINGING STEPS

Date: _____

1.  Sing the following exercises using relaxed, open vowel sounds.

2. Sing the following exercises using the correct tonic sol-fa syllables.

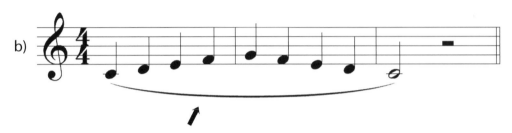

a)

b)

i) What is this curved line called? _____

ii) What does this line instruct the singer to do? _____

STEPS ON THE STAFF

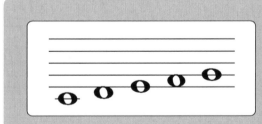

Notes moving in steps on the staff move from
line - space - line - space - line.

1. Fill in the missing stepping notes. Use **quarter** notes.

a)

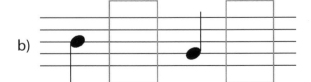

b)

FULL VOICE WORKBOOK - INTRODUCTORY LEVEL

Stepping Up
Tonic sol-fa syllables are sung in their ascending order.

> DO RE MI FA SO

Stepping Down
Tonic sol-fa syllables are sung in descending order.

> SO FA MI RE DO

1. Write the tonic sol-fa syllable a **step** higher.

a) **DO** _RE_   b) **MI** _____   c) **LA** _____   d) **RE** _____

2. Write the tonic sol-fa syllable a **step** lower.

a) **DO'** _TI_   b) **MI** _____   c) **LA** _____   d) **RE** _____

PERFORMANCE ASSESSMENT # 1

Choose one memorized song and perform it for your teacher.

Performances will be marked accordingly:

A Great job – keep up the good work.
B Good job – still room to improve.
C Needs work – improvement needed here.

Song: _____

	A	B	C
1. Did the singer sing/speak clearly throughout the song?	A	B	C
2. Did the singer breathe correctly?	A	B	C
3. Did the singer sing expressively?	A	B	C
4. Did the singer demonstrate proper singing posture?	A	B	C
5. _____	A	B	C

Teacher comments:

SINGING SKIPS

Date: _____

1.  Sing the following exercises using relaxed, open vowel sounds.

2. Sing the following exercises slowly, making sure you do not "scoop" into the notes.

a)

b)

3. Discuss with your teacher the difference between singing steps and singing skips.

4. Discuss with your teacher which exercise is more challenging.

SKIPS ON THE STAFF

These exercises are moving in **skips**. Notice the pattern of **line-line-line** or **space-space-space**.

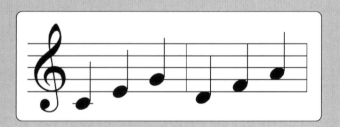

1. Fill in the missing **skipping** notes. Use **quarter** notes.

a)

b)

Skipping Up
Tonic sol-fa syllables skip over a syllable in ascending order.

| DO | RE | MI | FA | SO |

Skipping Down
Tonic sol-fa syllables skip over a syllable in descending order.

| SO | FA | MI | RE | DO |

1. Write the tonic sol-fa syllable a **skip** higher.

a) **DO** MI   b) **MI** _____   c) **LA** _____   d) **RE** _____

2. Write the tonic sol-fa syllable a **skip** lower.

a) **DO'** LA   b) **MI** _____   c) **LA** _____   d) **RE** _____

3. Fill in the missing skipping tonic sol-fa syllables.

a) **DO** MI **SO**   b) **RE** _____ **LA**   c) **MI** _____ _____

LESSON REVIEW: NOTES MOVING IN STEPS AND SKIPS

1. Sing **DO, MI, SO** without assistance from the piano. *(1 mark)*

2. Fill in the blanks below. *(1 mark each)*

   a) Notes moving in **skips** move:

   line to _____ to _____ , or space to _____ to _____ .

   b) Notes moving in **steps** move:

   line to _____ to _____ .

3. Identify if these notes are moving in skips or steps by circling the correct answer. *(3 marks)*

steps skips   steps skips   steps skips

10

SINGING STEPS AND SKIPS

Date: _____

1. Look at the following exercises. Identify if they are moving in steps, skips or both.

2. Sing the exercises using different vowels.

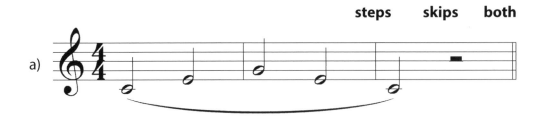

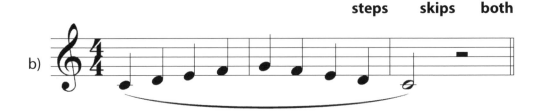

TONIC SOL-FA MOVING IN STEPS AND SKIPS

1. Label each group of syllables as skips (SK) or steps (ST).

a) **RE FA LA** | SK |
b) **SO FA MI** | |
c) **DO RE MI** | |

d) **DO' TI LA** | |
e) **DO MI SO** | |
f) **SO MI DO** | |

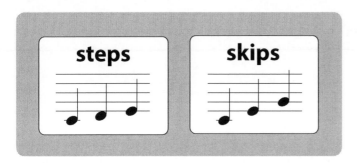

1. Listen to your teacher play three-note melodies at random.

   I can identify: ☐ steps ☐ skips

2. Listen carefully as your teacher plays or sings the following melodic examples **at random.**

3. Can you identify the melody that your teacher just played?

a)

b)

c)

d)

4. Play examples of steps and skips on the piano keyboard.

LESSON REVIEW: NOTES MOVING IN STEPS AND SKIPS

1. ✓ Look at a selection of music from your repertoire.

2. Can you find sections of the melody that move in steps? *(1 mark)*

3. Can you find sections of the melody that move in skips? *(1 mark)*

4. Fill in the missing note below to make the correct patterns of steps or skips. *(3 marks)*

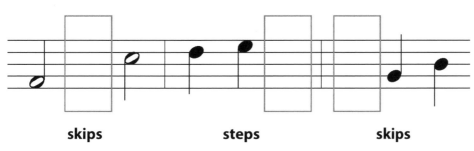

skips   steps   skips

$\frac{}{5}$

SINGING STEPS AND SKIPS

Date: _____

1.  Sing the following exercise. Use relaxed, open vowel sounds.

a)

2. Look at the exercise above and identify the following. *(1 mark each)*

   a) Note names C ___ ___ ___ ___ ___ ___

   b) Tonic sol-fa   ___ ___ ___ ___ ___ ___ ___

   c) Line or space   ___ ___ ___ ___ ___ ___ ___

20

NOTES ON THE STAFF

1. Write the following notes on the staff. Use **quarter notes**. *(1 mark each)*

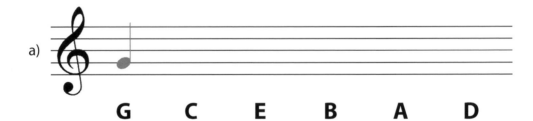

a)

G   C   E   B   A   D

2. Write the following notes on the staff. Use **half notes**. *(1 mark each)*

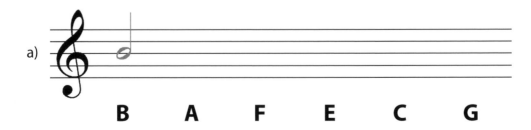

a)

B   A   F   E   C   G

10

FULL VOICE WORKBOOK - INTRODUCTORY LEVEL

1. ✎ Label each series of syllables as stepping up (↑) or stepping down (↓). *(3 marks)*

a) **MI FA SO** ☐   b) **MI RE DO** ☐   c) **DO' TI LA** ☐

2. ✎ Fill in the missing **skipping** notes. Use **half notes**. *(3 marks)*

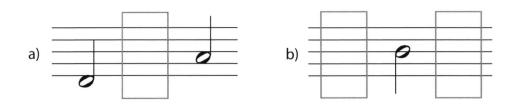

a)   b)

3. ✎ Write the tonic sol-fa syllable a **skip** higher. *(2 marks)*

a) **RE** _FA_   b) **MI** _____   c) **SO** _____

4. ✎ Draw lines connecting each pair of notes to the correct step or skip box. *(1 mark each)*

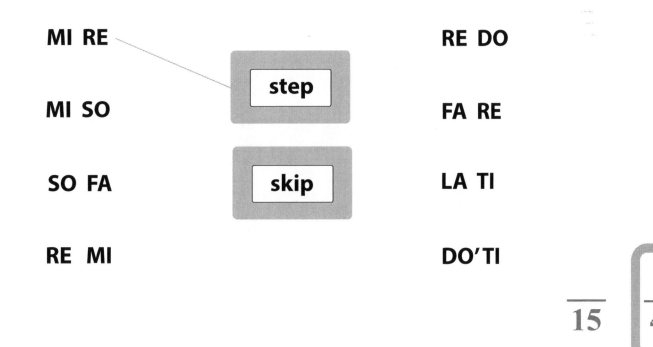

MI RE   **RE DO**

step

MI SO   **FA RE**

skip

SO FA   **LA TI**

RE MI   **DO' TI**

$\overline{15}$ $\overline{45}$

Are you ready to perform a memorized song for your teacher?
Use a performance assessment form at the back of your book (page 54) to record your progress.

Lesson Sixteen

SINGING STEPS AND SKIPS

Date: _____

1. 🖐 Clap and count the these exercises slowly.

2. 💬 Identify if the exercises are moving in steps, skips or both.

3. 🗣 Sing the exercises using different vowels.

a)

b)

TONIC SOL- FA: TRIAD

triad

A triad is a chord made up of the **first**, **third** and **fifth** notes of a scale. The notes move from line to line to line or space to space to space. Sing triads slowly. Be careful not to "scoop" or "slide" into these skipping notes.

DO'

TI

LA

SO

FA

MI

RE

DO

1. 🗣 Sing a **triad**.

2. 🗣 Sing the following patterns.

a) DO MI MI SO SO

b) SO SO MI MI DO

3. ✏ Write your own tonic sol-fa pattern using only **DO**, **MI** and **SO**.

4. 🗣 Sing your pattern.

<!-- five empty boxes -->

FULL VOICE WORKBOOK - INTRODUCTORY LEVEL

Bar line

Measure or bar

Bar lines are straight lines that divide the staff into measures or bars.

A **measure** or **bar** is a small section of the staff.

Time signatures are two numbers placed **beside the treble clef.** They tell us how many beats are allowed in each bar and show us how to count our music.

The **top number** tells us how many beats are allowed in each bar. The **bottom number** tells us what kind of note is counted as one beat. The 4 means quarter note, so in 4/4 time, we are allowed four beats in each bar.

1. Look at the following example and answer the questions below.

a) Circle the time signature.

b) How many beats are in each measure? _____

c) How many bar lines are there? _____

LESSON REVIEW: BAR LINES, MEASURES AND TIME SIGNATURES

1. Look carefully at a song from your repertoire to find the following. *(1 mark each)*

a) ☐ a time signature.

b) ☐ bar lines.

c) ☐ measures.

d) ☐ whole, half and quarter notes.

e) ☐ a treble clef.

5

QUARTER REST

Date: _____

Music is also written using symbols called **rests**. A rest is a moment of silence. Just like notes, rests are counted using steady "**counts**" or "**beats**".

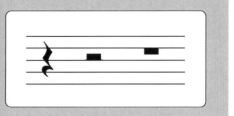

quarter rest

There is silence for **one** beat or count.

1. ✏️ Practice drawing **quarter rests** on the staff.

2. ✏️ Write the counts under the notes and rests.

3. ✋ Clap and count the following.

a)

1 2 3 4

b)

c)

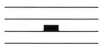

half rest

There is silence for **two** beats or counts.

1. ✎ Practice drawing **half rests** on the staff.

2. ✎ What space is the half rest in? _____

3. ✎ Write the counts under the notes.

4. ✋ Clap and count the following.

a)

1   2   3   4

b)

LESSON REVIEW: QUARTER REST AND HALF RESTS

1. ✎ Fill in the missing rests from each bar below. *(3 marks)*

2. ✎ Write the counts underneath the notes and rests. *(3 marks)*

3. ✋ Clap and count the rhythm. *(4 marks)*

$\overline{10}$

Lesson Eighteen

WHOLE REST

Date: _____

whole rest

There is silence
for **four** beats.

1. ✐ Practice drawing **whole rests** on the staff.

2. ✐ What space is the whole rest in? _____

3. ✐ Write the counts underneath the notes and rests.

4. ✋ Clap and count the rhythms.

a)

1 2 3 4

b)

A **whole rest** also indicates one entire measure of silence in **any time signature.**

5. ✐ Write the counts underneath the notes and rests.

6. ✋ Clap and count the rhythms.

a)

FULL VOICE WORKBOOK - INTRODUCTORY LEVEL

WRITING RESTS

1. Add one **quarter rest**, **half rest** or **whole rest** to complete each measure.

2. Write the counts underneath the notes and rests.

3. Clap and count the rhythms aloud.

a)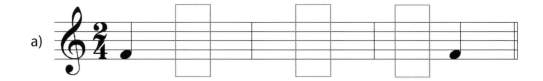

b)

c)

LESSON REVIEW: WRITING AND COUNTING RESTS

1. Look at the time signature and draw the correct rest in each bar. *(3 marks)*

2. Write the counts underneath the notes and rests. *(4 marks)*

3. Clap and count the rhythms aloud. *(3 marks)*

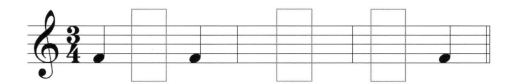

10

SINGING SCALES

Date: _____

major scale

The **C major scale** is eight notes ascending and descending in proper order. The notes move in **steps**. Have your teacher show you this scale on the piano.

1. Sing the C major scale.

a) ☐ Using tonic sol-fa. b) ☐ Using a vowel sound.
c) ☐ Using letter names. d) ☐ Using numbers.

LISTENING ACTIVITY

1. Look carefully at the rhythm examples below then listen carefully as your teacher claps the following one-bar rhythm examples randomly.

2. Can you identify which example your teacher performed?

3. Can you clap each rhythm back to your teacher?

a)

b)

c)

d)

1.  Clap and count the rhythms aloud.

a)

b)

c)

LESSON REVIEW: SINGING MAJOR SCALES

1. Practice singing the major scale, without help from the piano.
Perform the following scales at your next lesson for your teacher.

a) Sing a major scale ascending only, using any vowel. *(2 marks)*
b) Sing the major scale descending only, using any vowel. *(2 marks)*
c) Sing the major scale ascending and descending, using any vowel. *(3 marks)*
d) Sing the major scale ascending and descending using one breath. *(3 marks)*
e) Sing the major scale ascending and descending using a fast tempo. *(just for fun)*

____
10

Are you ready to perform a memorized song for your teacher?
Use a performance assessment form at the back of your book (page 54) to record your progress.

SINGING WITH DYNAMICS

Date: _____

Dynamics refer to the different volumes that a performer can sing. Singing with dynamics makes music exciting. Try singing these exercises with dynamics.

p
Piano "soft"

f
Forte "loud"

1. Sing these exercises using contrasting dynamics.

a)

b)

LISTENING ACTIVITY

1. Look carefully at the music in your repertoire book.

   Can you find dynamic markings in the score?

   Write down the dynamic markings below.

   _____

   _____

   _____

   _____

2. Listen carefully to your teacher play or sing a song or melody using different dynamics. Can you hear the difference between piano and forte?

3. Discuss with your teacher why the composer used the dynamics in your music.

1. 🖉 Draw a treble clef at the beginning of each staff.

2. 🖉 Name the notes.

a)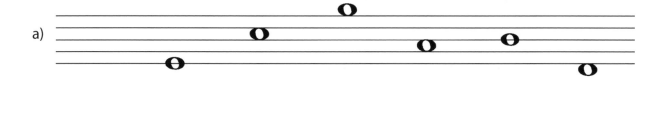

3. 🖉 Write the notes on the staff. Use **quarter** notes.

a)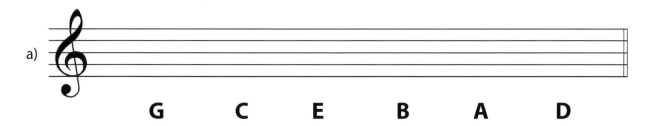

G   C   E   B   A   D

b)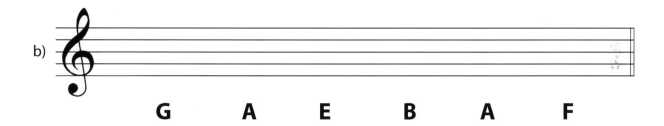

G   A   E   B   A   F

LESSON REVIEW: SINGING WITH DYNAMICS

1. 🖉 Choose a favourite repertoire piece and circle all dynamic markings with a pencil.

2. 🗣 Practice your song in the lesson and at home, focusing on performing all the dynamic markings.

3. 🗣 Perform this dynamic song at your next lesson for your teacher.
Can they hear you performing the contrasting dynamics? *(10 marks)*

_____
10

Introductory Level Review

TECHNICAL EXERCISES

Date: _____

1.  Sing the following exercise without assistance from the piano. *(1 mark)*

a)

2. Look at the exercise above and answer these questions. *(1 mark each)*

a) Is the above exercise moving in steps or skips? _____

b) What is the curved line connecting the notes called? _____

c) What does that marking tell you to do? _____

d) What kind of rest is at the end of the exercise? _____

___
5

WRITING MUSIC

1. Draw a **treble clef**.

2. Draw a **middle C** using a **whole note**.

3. Add the correct stem to each note below.

4. Name the notes.

C __ __ __ __ __ __ __

___
15

50   FULL VOICE WORKBOOK - INTRODUCTORY LEVEL

1. Name the notes aloud (A, B, C...). *(5 marks)*

2. Clap and count the rhythms aloud. *(5 marks)*

a)

b)

$\overline{10}$

STUDYING A SELECTION OF MUSIC

1. Look carefully at a song from your repertoire and find: *(1 mark each)*

a) ☐ a time signature.

b) ☐ bar lines.

c) ☐ measures.

d) ☐ whole, half and quarter notes.

e) ☐ a treble clef.

f) ☐ dynamic markings.

h) ☐ notes moving in skips.

I) ☐ notes moving in steps.

j) ☐ a slur marking.

k) ☐ a quarter rest.

$\overline{10}$ $\overline{40}$

Are you ready to perform a mini-recital for your teacher and family?
Use the mini-recital assessment form at the back of your book (page 55) to record your progress.

ADDITIONAL MUSIC WRITING ACTIVITIES

1. ✏️ Practice writing **notes, rests and treble clefs** on the staff below.

a)

b)

c)

d)

e)

f)

g)

h)

1.  Clap and count the rhythms aloud.

a)  ☐

b)  ☐

c)  ☐

d)  ☐

e)  ☐

f)  ☐

g) ☐

h)  ☐

Performance Assessments

PERFORMANCE ASSESSMENT # 2   Date: _____

Choose one memorized song and perform it for your teacher.

Performances will be marked accordingly:

A Great job – keep up the good work.
B Good job – still room to improve.
C Needs work – improvement needed here.

Song: _____

1. Did the singer appear comfortable and confident?	A B C
2. Did the singer sing/speak clearly throughout the song?	A B C
3. Did the singer demonstrate proper singing posture?	A B C
4. Did the singer perform all notes and rhythms correctly?	A B C

Teacher comments:

PERFORMANCE ASSESSMENT # 3   Date: _____

Choose one memorized song and perform it for your teacher.

Performances will be marked accordingly:

A Great job – keep up the good work.
B Good job – still room to improve.
C Needs work – improvement needed here.

Song: _____

1. Did the singer appear comfortable and confident?	A B C
2. Did the singer sing/speak clearly throughout the song?	A B C
3. Was this performance expressive and exciting?	A B C
4. Did the performer demonstrate proper singing posture?	A B C

Teacher comments:

Date: _____

Choose two or more songs and perform for your teacher, friends and family.
Record this performance so that teacher and student can review/discuss together.

Performances will be marked accordingly:　　**A Great job** – keep up the good work.
　　　　　　　　　　　　　　　　　　　　　　　B Good job – still room to improve.
　　　　　　　　　　　　　　　　　　　　　　　C Needs work – improvement needed here.

Songs:　_____ Composer: _____

　　　_____ Composer: _____

　　　_____ Composer: _____

1. Did the singer appear comfortable and confident?　　**A　B　C**

2. Did the singer use an introduction for this song?　　**A　B　C**

3. Was this performance expressive and exciting?　　**A　B　C**

4. Did this performer use contrasting dynamics effectively?　　**A　B　C**

5. How has this performer improved?

_____

_____

_____

6. What can this performer do to continuing improving?

_____

_____

7. Students, how did you feel about your performance?

_____

_____

_____

Teacher's comments:

REPERTOIRE LIST

Use this form to record all songs that you have learned and can perform from memory.

Date	Song	Composer	Performance
Sept 23	Lullaby	Nancy Telfer	Recital piece

1. Suggested listening/learning (new vocalists or repertoire to discover).

_____

_____

_____

2. Teacher comments.

_____

_____

Made in the USA
Monee, IL
29 July 2021